Contents

Seek and Find

Can you find these objects
in your book?

page 22

page 13

page 27

page 15

page 21

page 28

Solving Hidden Pictures puzzles develops figure-ground perception and improves the ability to establish object constancy and size relationships. Educators have shown that working on these puzzles can enhance a child's attention to detail, reinforce good work habits, increase word knowledge, and aid in developing self-confidence.

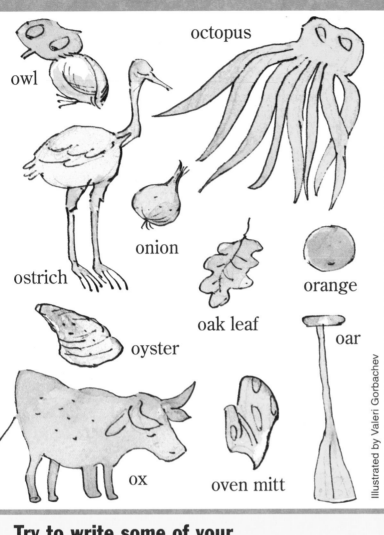

octopus

owl

onion

ostrich

oak leaf

orange

oyster

oar

Illustrated by Valeri Gorbachev

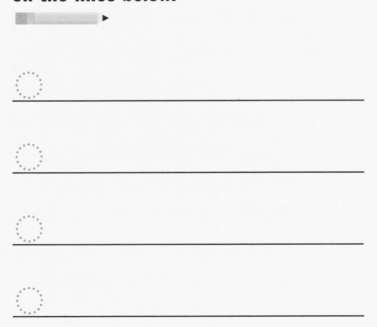

ox

oven mitt

Try to write some of your favorite words that begin with O on the lines below.

Answers on page 30

**These 8 funny things are happening in the scene.
Can you find them all?** Answers on page 30

Illustrated by Cathy Beylon

Imagine and Draw

Something silly is in the sandbox. Draw a picture of it here. CRAYON

Megan's grandfather is teaching her to play chess.

Can you find these hidden objects on the next page?

Answers on page 30

sea horse

bird

pencil

pie

heart

toothbrush

backpack

piggy bank

Can you guess the answer to each riddle? Use the Hidden Pictures® words if you need help.

I am round and good to eat.

Some kinds you'll like to buy.

Apple, peach, or pumpkin—

I am a yummy_____.

I do not neigh or gallop.

I never eat hay, of course.

My home lies underwater.

What am I? A _____.

Drop some coins inside me.

Hear them fall—*clink, clank.*

I'll make sure to save them.

I am your _____.

Load me up with books.

I can also hold a snack.

Make sure to zip my zipper.

I am a sturdy _____.

Can you find the Hidden Pictures below? When you finish, you can color in the

RABBITS

Color in a pocket in this box each time you find a pocket in the picture.

CRAYON

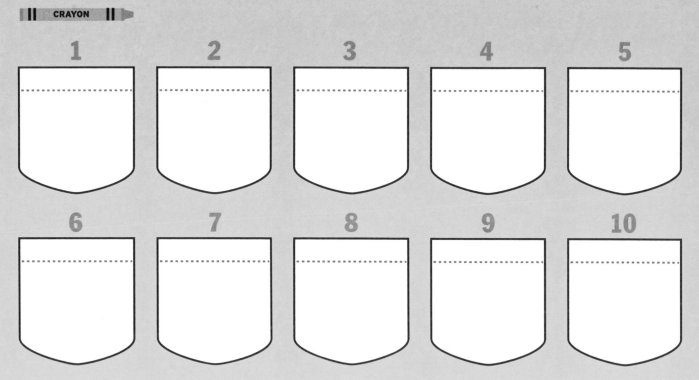

1   2   3   4   5

6   7   8   9   10

Connect the dots from Ⓐ to Ⓩ. When you finish, you will see something that you might carry in your pocket.

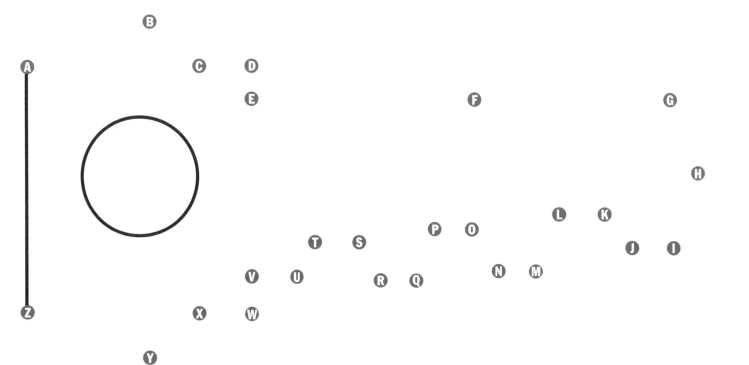

Mr. Donald's second-graders are working on arithmetic problems in the computer lab.

Can you find 8 Hidden Pictures® on the next page? Answers on page 31

dragonfly

oilcan

bell

slice of cake

measuring cup

ice scraper

toothbrush

drinking straw

Illustrated by Ron Lieser

Color in each shape that has a dot in it. When you finish, you will see something that you use with a computer. ‖ CRAYON ‖

Jacee and her little brother love to say hello to the fire fighters when they are washing their truck.

Can you find these Hidden Pictures® on the next page? Answers on page 31

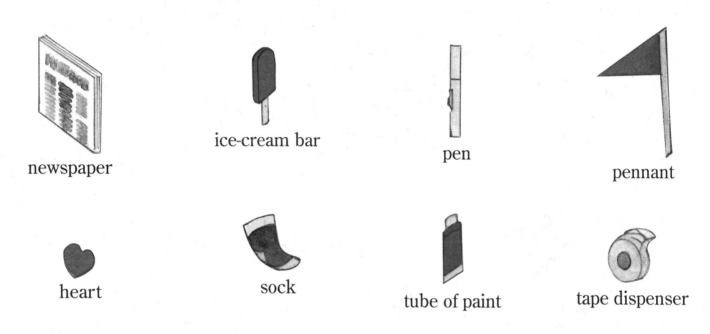

newspaper

ice-cream bar

pen

pennant

heart

sock

tube of paint

tape dispenser

Scavenger Hunt

Here are some more things to find:

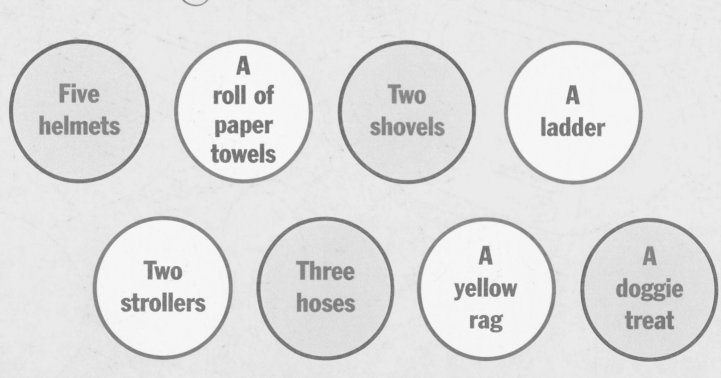

Five helmets

A roll of paper towels

Two shovels

A ladder

Two strollers

Three hoses

A yellow rag

A doggie treat

Can you find the Hidden Pictures below? When you finish, you can color in the

rest of the scene. **CRAYON** Answers on page 31 Illustrated by Timothy Davis

Mrs. Girard's piano students are performing for their parents and friends.

Can you find these items in the picture on the next page?
Be sure to find the right number of each. Answers on page 31

1 clock

2 cats

3 pairs of eyeglasses

4 hair ribbons

5 chairs

6 flowers

Use your crayons to decorate this program for the recital.

CRAYON

Mouse baked six heart-shaped cookies for her Valentine's Day party. There was no time to send an **invitation** to her friends Squirrel and Beaver, so she hurried off to find them.

On the way, Mouse met Turtle and Gopher by the 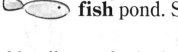 **fish** pond. She was always friendly, so she invited them to the party. Next, she met Porcupine, Bear, and Skunk by the **pine tree**. She invited them, too. At last, Mouse found Squirrel and Beaver by the old garden **gate**. "Please come to my party," she said. Then she scampered back to her **house**.

A Hidden Pictures® Rebus Story by Clare Mishica

"Oh my!" said Mouse as she counted her cookies. "I have too many friends and not enough cookies! This will be the worst party ever."

A moment later, Turtle and Gopher arrived with a big pink cake.

Next, Porcupine, Bear, and Skunk rang the **doorbell**. They brought their harmonicas to play songs. Squirrel and Beaver brought **apple** cider.

"My six little cookies have turned into **one** big party!" laughed Mouse as she served the cake.

"The best party ever!" agreed her friends.

Illustrated by Karen Stormer Brooks

Can you find the hidden objects from the story in this scene? Answers on page 32

butter knife   candy   key   coat hanger   lock   pencil

Each object is hidden two times—once in each scene. We found and circled the pencils. Can you find the others? Answers on page 32

horseshoe

wishbone

cherry

golf tee

spoon

slice of
fruit

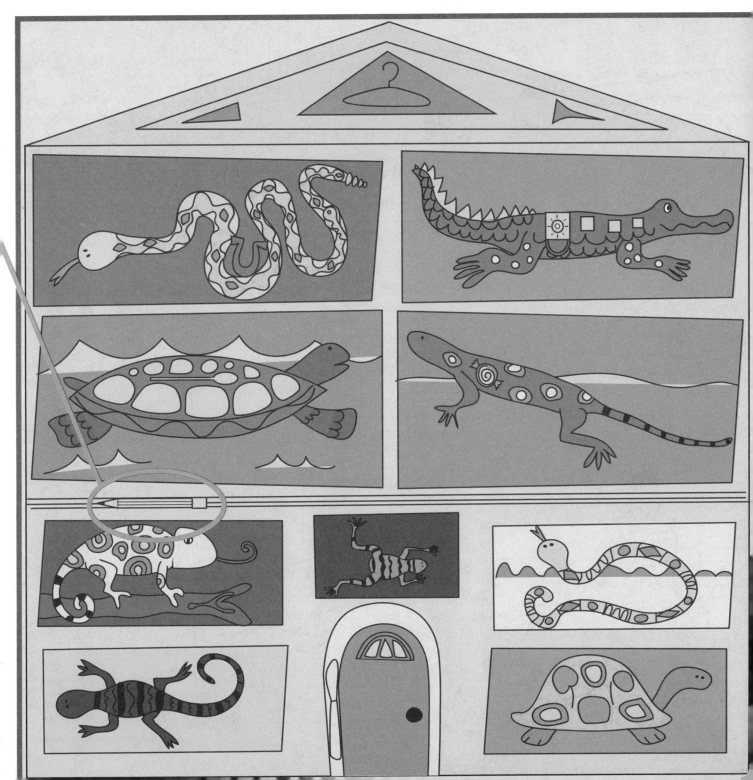

Can you find the Hidden Pictures below? When you finish, you can color in the

rest of the scene. **CRAYON** Answers on page 32

Illustrated by David Helton

Leo the artist is painting a beautiful sunset.

Can you find these shapes in the picture on the next page? Answers on page 32

Where do you go to watch the sun go down? Draw a picture of it here.

| CRAYON |

Be sure to write your name on your drawing when you are finished.

Hidden Pictures®

Jody and Royce are pasting some of their
best artwork into their scrapbooks.

There are 12 objects hidden in this picture. How many can you find?

Answers on page 32

spool

bat

paintbrush

sailboat

The names of the 12 objects are hidden below. Some are across. Others are up and down. Find and circle each word.

mug

snake

spoon

```
p  p  s  s  n  a  k  e
a  e  p  q  v  w  r  s
i  n  o  b  a  t  i  a
n  n  o  c  j  q  n  i
t  a  l  w  m  u  g  l
b  n  p  i  z  z  a  b
r  t  q  j  w  y  c  o
u  m  b  r  e  l  l  a
s  j  s  p  o  o  n  t
h  q  l  a  d  d  e  r
```

pizza

ring

ladder

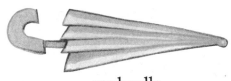
umbrella

pennant

Answers

Cover

Hidden Pictures® ABC pages 2–3

Silly Sandbox page 5

Chess Game pages 6–7

I am round and good to eat.
Some kinds you'll like to buy.
Apple, peach, or pumpkin—
I am a yummy **pie**.

I do not neigh or gallop.
I never eat hay, of course.
My home lies underwater.
What am I? A **sea horse**.

Drop some coins inside me.
Hear them fall—*clink, clank*.
I'll make sure to save them.
I am your **piggy bank**.

Load me up with books.
I can also hold a snack.
Make sure to zip my zipper.
I am a sturdy **backpack**.

Pet Show pages 8–9

Answers

Pocket Search **pages 10–11**

It's a key!

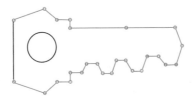

Scavenger Hunt

Five helmets
Three are hanging on the wall.
Two fire fighters each are wearing one.

A roll of paper towels
Look on top of the fire truck.

Two shovels
A fire fighter is carrying them.

A ladder
It is hanging on the fire truck.

Two strollers
Jacee's little brother is riding in one.
Jacee's teddy bear is riding in one.

Three hoses
Two are folded on top of the fire truck.
One is on the floor.

Computer Lab **pages 12–13**

It's a computer mouse!

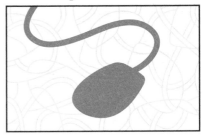

A yellow rag
A fire fighter is using it to wipe the door of the fire truck.

A doggie treat
Look near the dog's nose.

Fire Station **pages 14–15**

Skateboard Park **pages 16–17**

Music Recital **page 19**

Answers

Valentine's Day Party page 21

Double Hidden Pictures® pages 22–23

On the Boardwalk pages 24–25

Find the Shapes page 27

Hidden Pictures Hidden Words pages 28–29